Map Skills
for Key Stage 2
Pam Robson

CW00346996

The author, Pam Robson, is an experienced primary teacher with a particular interest in geography.

The consultant, Stephen Watts, is a teacher trainer at Sunderland University and a Fellow of the Royal Geographical Society.

Teacher's Notes

What is good classroom practice?

Ofsted inspection findings since 1992 highlight the need to integrate geographical skills into suitable real contexts. They also recommend that the teaching of geographical skills and investigations of places and themes should feed upon each other as part of one integrated scheme of work.

Relevant documents to consult are:

Ofsted	a Review of Inspection Findings – 1993/4
QCA	Expectations in Geography at Key Stages 1 and 2 – 1997
QCA	Geography and the Use of Language – 1997

In the light of the above recommendations, teachers should select worksheets that have relevance to real contexts, to which their pupils can relate. They should be used in conjunction with class investigations about particular places and themes rather than as isolated learning tools.

Literacy

The worksheets have been designed to support the requirements of the National Literacy Project. Teachers will find links with literature and will also be able to encourage research skills using appropriate vocabulary, including the use of structural guiders.

An investigative approach

The focus of enquiry is indicated at the top of each sheet. Key questions then open up specific topics and themes to be investigated. On some sheets relevant discussion points are raised. Symbols highlight each area of activity:

Key:

 key question  investigation discussion

How to use this book

The worksheets have been structured in accordance with national curriculum requirements to reinforce and extend the basic geographical skills and concepts covered in the KS1 title 'Map Skills'. Teachers will find that worksheets in the KS1 title will also be appropriate for children working at the early stages of KS2. Similarly worksheets in the KS2 book may also be appropriate for some children working at the later stages of KS1.

Teachers can also use relevant worksheets from this title with children working at the early stages of KS3.

Teachers are advised to work progressively through the structured investigations. Alternatively, specific worksheets relating to one particular focus of enquiry can be selected if used in sequence.

Materials

All teachers are aware of the need to be fully prepared, and organisation is generally accepted as being a key to success in the classroom. With this in mind, relevant information about resources and materials required for the worksheets is provided, on page 3.

Topic Web KS2
(with reference to National Curriculum requirements)

Geographical Skills *in the context of* **Places, and the four themes of Rivers, Weather, Settlement and Environmental Change (core of the topic web)**

- collect and record evidence (2b)
- analyse evidence, draw conclusions and communicate findings (2c)
- use geographical vocabulary (3a)
- undertake fieldwork (3b)
- make plans and maps (3c)
- use globes, maps and plans (3d)
- use secondary sources of evidence (3e)
- use IT to present evidence (3f)

Linked subject areas are:

1 English
Speaking and Listening:

- report and describe observations (1a)
- use increasingly varied vocabulary (3b)

Reading:

- read and use a wide range of sources of information (1b)
- use organisational devices in books (2c)
- read for different purposes (2c)
- use dictionaries and glossaries (2c)
- note the meaning and use of newly encountered words (2c)
- represent information in different forms (2c)

Writing:

- write reports, instructions and explanations (1c)
- write for unfamiliar audiences e.g in a style appropriate for a guidebook (2a)
- use different forms of handwriting for different purposes e.g labelling maps (2e)

2 Maths
Shape, Space and Measures:

- apply measuring skills (1e)
- 2D and 3D shapes / classify shapes (2b)
- use map references (3b)
- use right angles, fractions of turns and degrees (3c)
- make sensible estimates in everyday situations (4a)
- use measuring instruments and scales (4b)
- find perimeters (4c)

Handling Data:

- access and collect data (1b)
- use computers (1c)

3 History
Romans, Anglo-Saxons and Vikings:

- the legacy of settlement (2a, 2b, 2c)

4 Science
Living things in their environment:

- that different plants and animals are found in different habitats (5a)

5 Art and Design
Displaying geographical information / labelling / designing keys

Resources

Worksheet number & Focus of Enquiry	Resources needed
1 Plans	a collection of 3D objects eg dice, toy cars, balls; drawing paper and pencils
2 Plans	colouring media
3 Plans	photographs or pictures of various kinds of housing; colouring media
4 Scale	squared paper – half centimetre, one centimetre and two centimetre; pencils
5 Scale	centimetre rulers; pencils, tape measures
6 Scale	atlases; centimetre rulers
7 Scale	colouring media; centimetre rulers; O S maps of the locality
8 Scale	metre sticks; tape measures; centimetre rulers; squared paper; sketching paper; pencils
9 Collecting Data	OS maps of the locality; pencils; computer access to record data (optional)
10 Compass Direction	colouring media
11 Compass Direction	atlases; pencils
12 Compass Direction	360 degree protractors; centimetre rulers; pencils; magnetic compasses for field work
13 Compass Direction	pencils; drawing paper
14 Reading Maps (2 sheets)	centimetre rulers; string; OS maps of the locality
15 Scale	OS Maps and atlases; centimetre rulers
16 Reading Maps (2 sheets)	children should be familiar with the story 'James and the Giant Peach' by Roald Dahl; colouring media; examples of a variety of maps eg relief, political, pictorial
17 Reading Maps	'The Diary of Anne Frank'; travel brochures and photographs of Amsterdam; colouring media; centimetre rulers; pencils
18 Grid References (2 sheets)	nursery rhyme 'Oranges and Lemons'; dice; coloured counters; map of the old city of London (optional); OS maps (optional)
19 Grid References	colouring media; OS maps
20 Grid References	colouring media; OS maps
21 Labelling Maps	atlases with relief maps of the British Isles; colouring media; dictionaries; pencils; rulers
22 Settlements	OS maps of localities in the British Isles with place names originating from Saxon, Viking or Celtic settlements eg Yorkshire, Hampshire, Cornwall
23 Labelling Maps	outline map of the world; atlases; colouring media; pencils; rulers
24 Geographical Vocabulary	previous worksheets; dictionaries; pencils NB Teachers may want to provide the second letter of the missing words if children need some extra help.
25 Latitude and Longitude	a globe; atlases
26 Latitude and Longitude	the whole peel from an orange; a variety of maps produced from different projections, including a cylindrical projection; a globe
27 Continents and Countries	atlases; colouring media; a globe
28 Latitude and Longitude	atlases; colouring media
29 Latitude and Longitude	atlases; pencils
30 Continents and Countries	atlases; colouring media; photographs and pictures of Kenya and the flag of Kenya
31 Time Zones	atlases; a globe
32 Latitude and Longitude	a climate map of the world showing prevailing winds; pencils
33 Land Use	atlases; pictures of the crops discussed; colouring media
34 Cities of Europe	centimetre rulers; pencils; travel brochures advertising journeys to European cities
35 Rivers of Europe	atlases with relief maps of European countries, including the British Isles, showing that rivers flow from high ground, downhill to the sea; pencils; colouring media; outline maps of world
36 Pollution	outline map of the world; pictures or photographs of wild animals of the Persian Gulf; O.S maps of the locality (optional); colouring media; pencils

Teacher's checklist of geographical skills

Names		is able to use appropriate geographical vocabulary	is able to describe and interpret their surroundings	has undertaken fieldwork	has made maps and plans at a variety of scales, using symbols and keys	has used co-ordinates and four-figure references	has followed routes, measuring directions and distance	is able to use the index pages of an atlas	has used secondary sources of evidence

Pupil's checklist

....

Name.. **Date**..................

1   I know that a plan is a bird's eye view ....

2   I understand that distances on maps and plans are shown using scales.

     A small scale map shows a .... area.

     A large scale map shows a .... area.

3   I have measured direction and distance on maps.

     My school is .... kilometres from my home.

     The direction that I look through my classroom window is ....

4   I know how to use a 16-point compass ....

5   I know how to use 4-figure grid references on an ordnance survey map. ....

     The 4-figure grid reference for my school is ....

6   I know how to use 6-figure grid references on an ordnance survey map. ....

     The 6-figure grid reference for my school is ....

7   I know how to use an atlas index.

     The atlas reference for London is: country .... page , , , , , , , , , ,

     latitude/longitude ....

8   I have used secondary sources, such as photographs, to learn about places.

     I looked at photographs of ....

     From the photographs of .... I learned that

     ....

     ....

9   I know how to label a map neatly.

     This is an example of my printing in lower case (small) letters

     ....

10   I have compiled my own dictionary of geographical words.

     The first word in my dictionary is ....

     The last word in my dictionary is ....

What is a bird's eye view?

A bird in the air sees everything from above. It has a bird's eye view. The higher it flies the more it can see. Plans and maps usually show a bird's eye view of objects and places.

Look at the pictures below. Imagine what each object would look like from above. Draw a ring around the correct bird's eye view (or plan) for each picture.

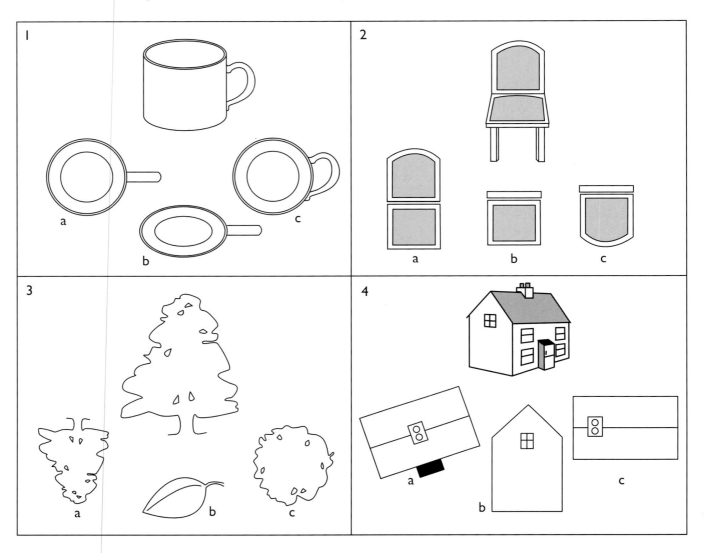

Choose three classroom objects. Look at each object from the side and draw pictures of what you see. Now look at each object from above, a bird's eye view, and draw what you can see.

This is a bird's eye view. What is it?

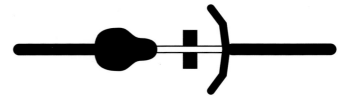

What differences are there between a side view and a bird's eye view?

What does a park look like from above?

Compare the picture of the park (A) in the small town of Wigglethrop with the bird's eye view, or plan (B), of the park.

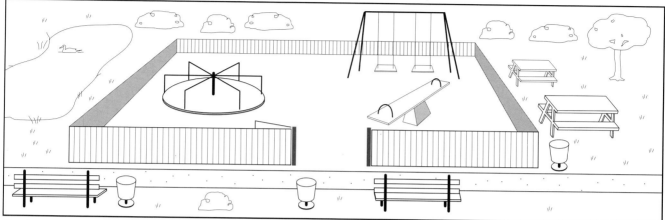

A A picture of Wigglethrop Park

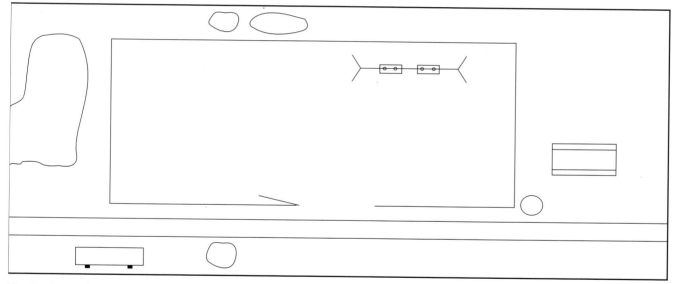

B A plan of Wigglethrop Park

Some objects are missing from the plan. Can you draw them in the right places? Remember to draw a bird's eye view.

On the picture and the plan:

1 Colour the duck yellow.
2 Colour the litter bins red.
3 Colour the swings orange.
4 Colour the roundabout purple.

5 Colour the picnic tables and benches brown.
6 Colour the pond blue.
7 Colour the seesaw pink.
8 Colour the bushes and trees green.

 Look at your playground. What do you think it looks like from above?

What does a plan of a town look like?

Compare the picture of Wigglethrop with the plan of the town.
Why does the park look so small? Can you see everything on the ground clearly?
What would you see if you were even higher in the sky?

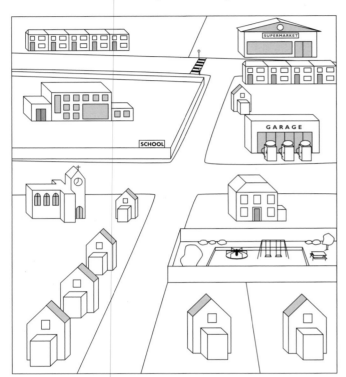

Picture of Wigglethrop

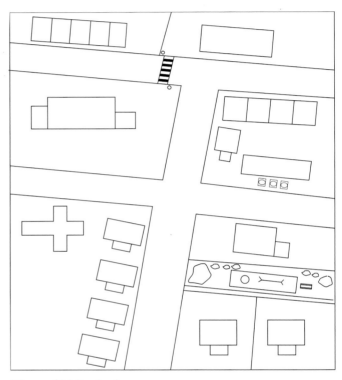

Plan of Wigglethrop

1   Look at all the buildings.

What kind of homes can you see in Wigglethrop? . . . .

. . . .

Colour all the detached houses red in the picture and on the plan. Colour the
terraced houses blue.

2   What other buildings can you see in the plan?

a . . . .   **c** . . . .

b . . . .   **d** . . . .

Colour them in different colours. Make sure the picture and the plan match.

3   What kinds of homes are found near your school? . . . .

. . . .

What other kinds of homes are found in Britain? What other kinds of homes are there in
other parts of the world?

How is an object drawn to scale?

An object can be made to look larger or smaller than it really is, without altering its shape, by drawing to *scale*. This means there is a *ratio* between the real size and the size of the drawing. Look at the picture of the butterfly drawn on 2 cm square paper.

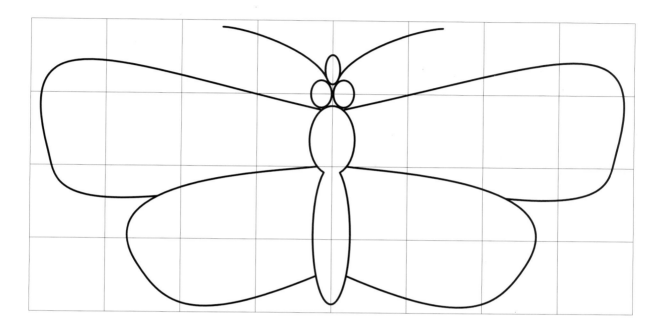

Find out how to reduce the size of the butterfly.

You can draw the picture half the size by copying the shape, exactly, on to 1 cm square paper. Your new picture is drawn to the ratio 1:2. It is half the size.

Now draw the butterfly on half cm square paper. This butterfly looks very tiny! The ratio of the tiny butterfly to the largest butterfly is 1:4. It is one quarter of the size.

We could also say that the largest butterfly is four times as big as the tiny one, so the ratio is also 4:1.

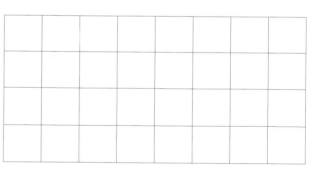

ratio: 1:2

ratio: 1:4

Find out how to enlarge a shape. Draw a mouse or a cat shape on half cm square paper. Now transfer the shape on to 2 cm square paper.

What is the ratio?   . . . .

Who might need to make scale drawings in their work?

How do I work out real size from a scale?

Maps and plans are usually drawn to scale. Everything is drawn much smaller than it really is but the shapes stay the same. When an object is drawn to scale there is a ratio between the measurements of the real object and measurements of the drawing.

Look at this plan of a box. It is drawn to scale.
The plan is drawn to a ratio of 1:2.
1 cm on the drawing stands for 2 cm on the real box.
Each side of the box measures 2 cm. So each side of the real box measures 4 cm.

ratio: 1:2

Use a ruler to find out how long the sides of these boxes are really.

1   . . . . cm

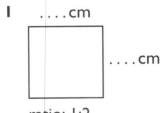

. . . . cm

ratio: 1:2

2   . . . . cm

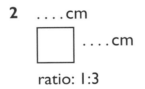

. . . . cm

ratio: 1:3

3   . . . . cm

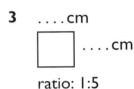

. . . . cm

ratio: 1:5

Which is the biggest box really? . . . .

These pictures need to be framed. Look at the ratio and use a ruler to discover which picture fits which frame.

A ← cm →
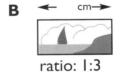
ratio: 1:8

B ← cm →
ratio: 1:3

C ← cm →
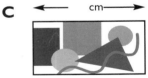
ratio: 1:6

1
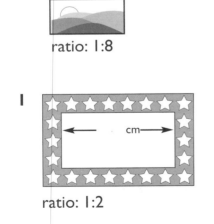
← cm →
ratio: 1:2

2
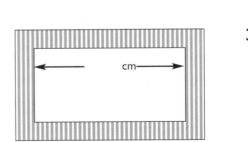
cm
ratio: 1:4

3
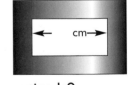
← cm →
ratio: 1:9

Picture **A** fits frame . . . . .   Picture **B** fits frame . . . . .   Picture **C** fits frame . . . . .

Measure the height and width of your classroom door, then draw it to a ratio of 1:20. This means 1 cm on your drawing stands for 20 cm on the real door. Write the scale next to your drawing.

How is scale shown on maps?

Maps use scales. By using a scale, long distances on the ground can be shown by short distances on a map.

Scale is shown in two ways on a map:

A as a *representative fraction,* for example, 1:10000. This means that 1 cm on the map stands for 10000 cm (100 m) on the ground (remember that 100 cm = 1 metre).

B on a *scale bar* on which a line is divided into centimetres so that 1 cm stands for a certain number of metres or kilometres, for example:

0	50m	100	150m

These lines have been drawn to scale. Measure them and work out how long they are really.

1 Scale: 1:3000 (1 cm stands for 30 m)

   a ——————— . . . . metres

   b ——————————— . . . . metres

   c —————————————————— . . . . metres

2 Scale: 1:15000 (1 cm stands for 150 m)

   a ———— . . . . metres

   b —————— . . . . metres

   c —————————————— . . . . metres

3 Scale Bar: |———|———|———| kilometres (1 cm stands for 500 m)
                    0   0.5   1   1.5

   a ———— . . . . kilometres

   b —————————————— . . . . kilometres

   c —————————— . . . . kilometres

4 Scale Bar: |———|———|———| kilometres (1 cm stands for 2 km)
                    0   2   4   6

   a ———— . . . . kilometres

   b ———————————— . . . . kilometres

   c ——————————————————— . . . . kilometres

  Look in an atlas. Write down some of the scales used and on which maps they appear. Say what 1 cm stands for on each scale.

How does the scale on a map or plan work?

This is a plan of a fairground. The key tells you what the symbols stand for.
Colour the symbols in the key, then use the same colours on the plan.

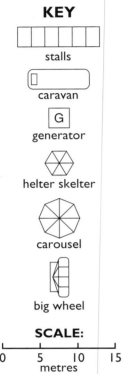

KEY

stalls

caravan

generator

helter skelter

carousel

big wheel

SCALE:

0   5   10   15
     metres

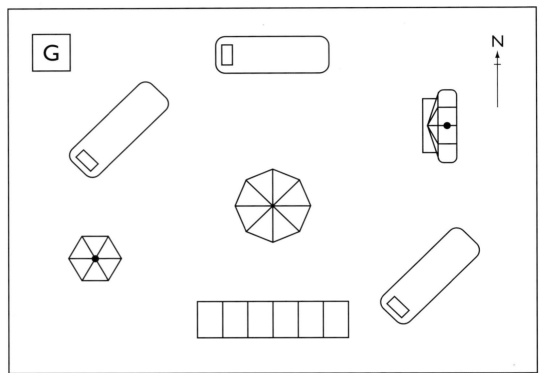

Use a ruler to measure the distances on the plan. Then use the scale to answer these questions.

1 On the plan the length of the field is . . . . . . centimetres.

   The real field is . . . . . . metres long.

2 On the plan the width of the field is . . . . . . centimetres.

   The real field is . . . . . . metres wide.

3 On the plan the perimeter of the field is . . . . . . centimetres.

   the perimeter of the real field is . . . . . . metres.

4 The distance from the spot on the Big Wheel to the spot on the Helter Skelter is . . . . . . centimetres.

   The distance between the Big Wheel and the Helter Skelter is really . . . . . . metres.

5 What is in the north-west corner of the fairground? . . . .

Look at an Ordnance Survey map of your area. Read the scale. Measure a straight line from your home to your school. How far is that really? How could you work out the distance by road, from the map?

How can a room be drawn to scale?

This is a rough sketch for a plan of a bedroom. On the squared paper one square represents 50 cm (half a metre). Now draw the details in the sketch, to scale, on the squared paper. Count the squares carefully to make sure everything is in the correct position. Design a colour key for your plan. Write the scale next to your plan.

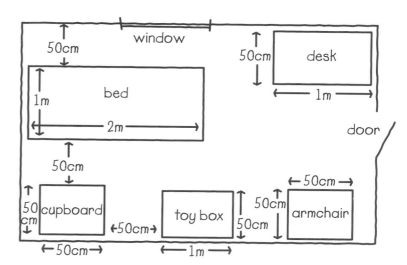

KEY

Does the scale plan look different from the rough sketch?

Draw a plan of your classroom to scale.
You will need a metre stick or tape measure, a pencil and ruler, a sketch pad and squared paper.
First take careful measurements and note them down on a rough sketch, showing the position of things in the room. Then draw an accurate plan to scale on squared paper. One square will represent one metre in the classroom.

How do I carry out a housing survey?

Use an Ordnance Survey map to select roads that are close to your home or school. Use the tally chart below to record how many different homes you observe there.

Important When carrying out your housing survey:
- ask a grown-up first
- always stay with a friend.

A housing survey Street names	Blocks of flats	Semi-detached houses	Detached houses	Terraced houses	Bungalows	Total

General conclusions

Create a computer spreadsheet or database to display your housing survey information. What else does your information tell you about your locality?

Why are landmarks important?

Colour the plan of the beach. Complete the eight point compass rose.

The sea is due . . . . from the beach.

Note *A groyne is a wall built across a beach as far as the sea. It prevents the sand from being washed away by the sea.*

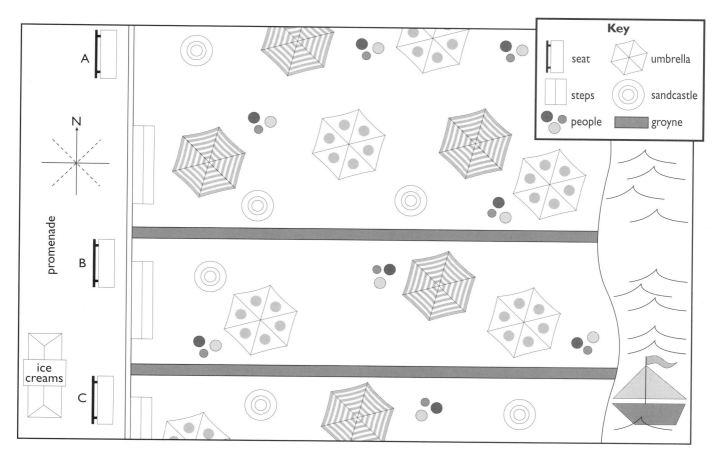

 How many striped umbrellas? . . . . . .   How many flights of steps lead to the beach? . . . . . .

How many sandcastles? . . . . . .   How many seats are there on the promenade? . . . . . .

You are looking for your family on the crowded beach. They are sitting due east of a flight of steps. To the west of the place they are sitting is a sandcastle. To the south of the place they are sitting is a groyne. To the north is a striped umbrella. Can you locate your family? Mark the spot clearly.

In which direction will you walk from your family's position on the beach to buy an ice cream? . . . .

In which direction will a person sitting on seat A be looking if they are watching the sailing boat? . . . .

 Look outside the classroom window and select a landmark. Now describe the position of an object in relation to the landmark.

What are compass directions?

We use compass directions to describe where one place is in relation to another, because a magnetic compass needle always points towards north. Look at a map of North America. Do you think Canada is *above* the USA? It may *look* as if it is on a map, but Canada is really *north* of the USA. The USA is *south* of Canada.

Look at the drawing of the compass. Eight-point directions are marked for you. Fill in the missing 16-point directions; the first ones are done for you.

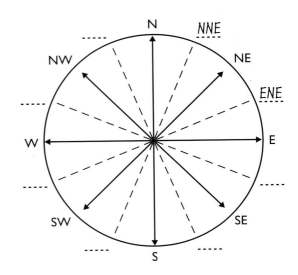

 Now use the compass to give compass directions to describe the approximate positions of these places in Wales:

1 Bangor is . . . . of Aberystwyth.

2 Milford Haven is . . . . of Swansea.

3 Newport is . . . . of Cardiff.

4 Swansea is . . . . of Brecon.

5 Aberystwyth is

. . . . of Bangor.

. . . . of Brecon

. . . . of Milford Haven

. . . . of Swansea

. . . . of Cardiff

. . . . of Newport.

 Use an atlas to find a map of the U.K. on which counties are named. Find the county in which you live. In which part of the county is your home: north, south, east or west? If you live in a large city, look on a large scale street map of the city to find your street.

What is a bearing?

Compass directions can also be given as degrees or *bearings*.

The bearing from north to east means turning through an angle of 90°.

This bearing is 090°.

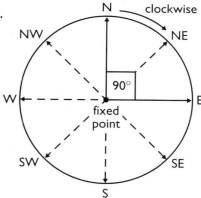

> **Note** *A bearing is always measured from a fixed point. From that fixed point, north is established. Bearings are measured clockwise from north.*

Calculate the bearings for:

I NE . . . .   **2** SE . . . .   **3** W . . . .   **4** SW . . . .   **5** S . . . .

Look at this scale plan showing various landmarks. Use the spots as measuring points. Draw lines joining each landmark to the fixed point. Use the scale to calculate the distances between the landmarks and the fixed point. Now use a 360° protractor to measure the bearing of each landmark, clockwise from north at the fixed point.

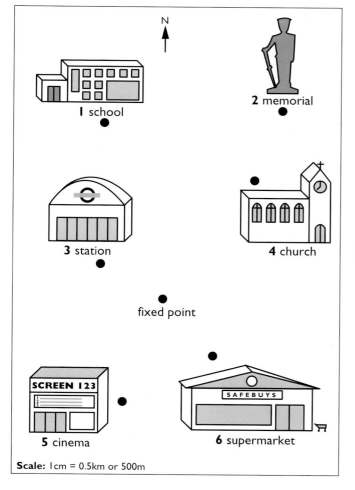

Scale: 1cm = 0.5km or 500m

Landmark	Distance	Bearing
I school	. . . . km	. . . .°
2 memorial	. . . . km	. . . .°
3 station	. . . . km	. . . .°
4 church	. . . . km	. . . .°
5 cinema	. . . . km	. . . .°
6 supermarket	. . . . km	. . . .°

Establish a fixed point in your school playground. Measure and map visible landmarks inside the playground. Use a compass.

How can I give directions when there are no landmarks?

 This plan of a maze has no landmarks. Find the route to the centre of this maze and draw it in. Then write down compass directions and distances.
The first directions have been done for you.

Into the maze

1 go north, forward 3 squares

2 turn east, go forward 4 squares

3 turn north, go forward 3 squares

4 ....

....

....

....

....

....

....

Now write down directions to get back out of the maze.

Out of the maze

1 go east, forward 2 squares

....

....

....

....

....

....

....

....

....

Can you design your own maze? Ask a friend to find the route to the centre.

What does a large-scale street map show?

Look at the plan of the small town of Bilton, on the separate sheet. Read the scale bar. You will need a ruler to answer these questions.

1   How far is it really from the petrol station to the church by road?   . . . . metres

2   What is the real distance between the synagogue and the post office by road?   . . . . metres

3   Work out the shortest route by road from the police station to the school. How far is it really?   . . . . metres

4   I turn right outside the library and walk eastwards for 500 metres. Then I turn right and walk SE for 200 metres. What is my destination?   . . . .

5   I leave the park by the gate in West End Lane. I turn left and walk due west for 50 metres. I turn left again and walk south for 150 metres. I turn right and walk west for 400 metres. What is my destination?   . . . .

6   Give directions for the two possible routes from the public house to the railway station.

route **a** . . . .

Distance . . . . metres

route **b** . . . .

Distance . . . . metres

Which route is shorter? . . . .

7   Give distance and direction for the shortest route from the bus stop outside the supermarket to the church.

. . . .

. . . .

Distance . . . . metres

Look at an O.S. street map of your locality. What symbols are used? What is the scale? Write down directions from your home to school.

How could you work out distances on a map where the road was bendy, not straight?

Plan of Bilton

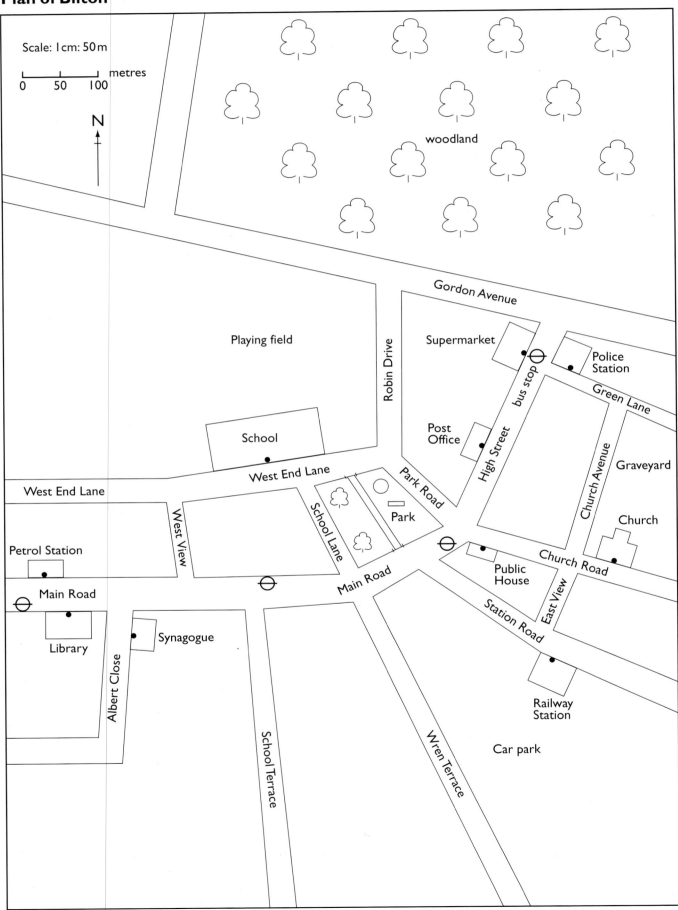

Scale: 1 cm: 50 m

0   50   100   metres

N

woodland

Gordon Avenue

Playing field

Robin Drive

Supermarket

bus stop

Police Station

Green Lane

Post Office

High Street

School

West End Lane

West End Lane

School Lane

Park Road

Park

Church Avenue

Graveyard

Church

West View

Petrol Station

Main Road

Main Road

Public House

Church Road

East View

Library

Albert Close

Synagogue

Station Road

School Terrace

Wren Terrace

Railway Station

Car park

What are the differences between large-scale maps and small-scale maps?

Investigate the three maps below. How are they different? Are they similar in any way?

Talk about your ideas with a friend.

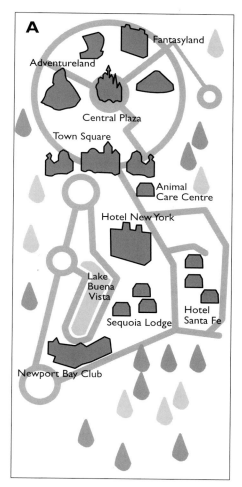

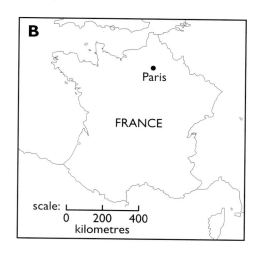

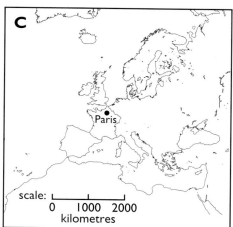

Plan A is a *very large scale* plan, or map, of Disneyland, Paris.

Map B is a *much smaller scale* map showing a wider area
but less detail.
Scale: 1:20 000 000
(1cm stands for 20 million cm *or* 1cm: 200km)

Map C is a *very small scale* map, part of a map of the
whole world.
Scale:1:100 000 000
(1cm stands for 1 hundred million cm *or* 1cm: 1000km)

Draw linear scale bars for these representative scales:

1 1: 3000 ⊢___|___|___⊣ metres   **5** 1: 1 000 000 _____ kilometres
                       0   30

2 1: 25 000 _____ metres   **6** 1: 20 000 000 _____ kilometres

3 1: 2500 _____ metres   **7** 1: 2 000 000 _____ kilometres

4 1: 100 000 _____ kilometres   **8** 1: 5 000 000 _____ kilometres

A street map is . . . . scale.   A map of the world is . . . . scale.

Look at scales on O.S. maps and atlas maps. What do you notice?

What is a pictorial map?

Read the story *of James and the Giant Peach* by Roald Dahl.
Then complete the maps.

1 7 year old James lives with two horrid aunts – fat Aunt Sponge and skinny
Aunt Spiker. They live in a house on top of a hill, from where James can see
for miles. In the middle of the front garden is an old peach tree. To the south
is a village and, in the distance, the ocean.

Colour the land between 50 and 100m above sea level yellow.
Colour the land between 100 and 200m above sea level orange.
Colour the land higher than 200m above sea level brown.
Colour the rest of the story map. Complete the key.

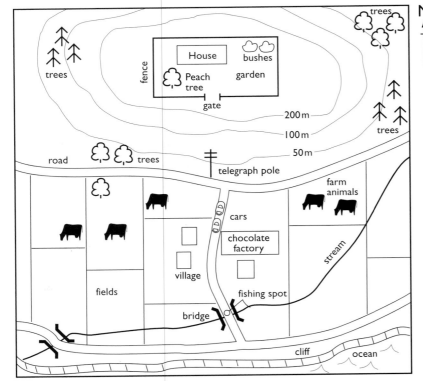

2 Magic crystals make a giant peach grow on the old peach tree. James crawls
inside the peach and finds a room full of giant minibeasts. Grasshopper, spider
and ladybird are sitting on chairs; centipede and earthworm are on a sofa.

Centipede bites through the stem of the peach and it rolls downhill towards
the ocean in the distance. First it squashes the two horrid aunts by the gate.
At the bottom of the hill it rolls over the road and flattens two cars and a
telegraph post. Farm animals scatter in all directions. It rolls through the
village leaving a hole in the wall of the chocolate factory. A man fishing loses
his rod. Finally the peach reaches the cliff top and falls into the ocean.

Continued on next page ▶

Draw the route taken by the peach on a pictorial map. The hill has been drawn for you. Fill in the objects that the giant peach rolls over in the right places on the map.

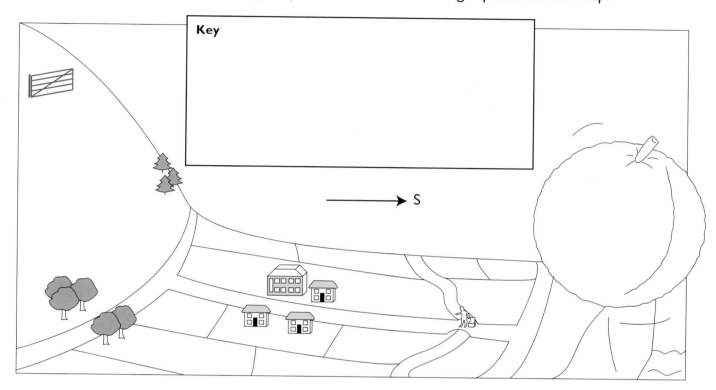

Key

S

3 James has lots of exciting adventures inside the peach. It is carried westwards, from the south coast of England, over the Atlantic Ocean to America. It lands in New York on top of the Empire State Building.

Mark the route of the flying peach from England to America.

Colour the map.

Is this map a pictorial map? How is it different from the map above?

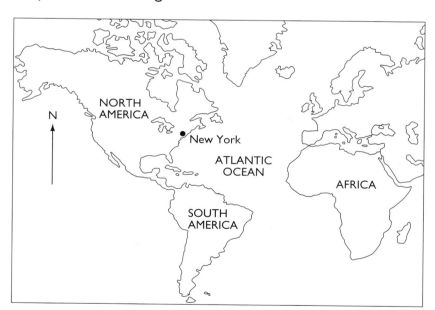

NORTH AMERICA

N

New York

ATLANTIC OCEAN

AFRICA

SOUTH AMERICA

The Empire State Building is a skyscraper 381m tall.

How high is the hill on which James lives with his Aunts?
Over . . . . m.

How high is Ben Nevis, the highest mountain in the UK?   . . . . m.

What other stories do you know that describe a fantastic journey?

What kind of landmarks can be shown on maps?

The diary of Anne Frank reveals details of her tragically short life. She was a German Jew, born in Frankfurt. In 1933, when she was four, Anne and her family went to live in Amsterdam, the Netherlands, because Jews were being badly treated in Germany.

On Anne's 13th birthday she and her family had to go into hiding when German Nazis took over the Netherlands. They hid upstairs in a secret apartment at 263 Prinsengracht. They hid there for two years. This is where Anne wrote her diary.

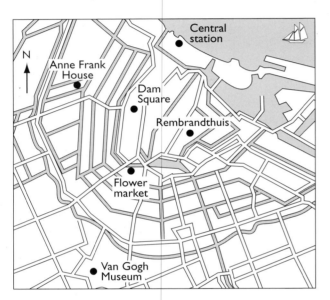

Amsterdam is a city of canals crossed by many bridges. Narrow streets are filled with cyclists. Tourists now visit 263 Prinsengracht.

1 Colour the canals (shown here in grey) blue.

2 Colour the bridges and roads that cross them red.

3 Anne Frank's house is . . . . of Dam Square.

4 The Van Gogh Museum is . . . . of Anne Frank's House.

5 Rembrandthuis is . . . . of the Central Station.

There are ferry routes between the UK and the Netherlands between:

a Harwich – Hook of Holland. The journey takes approximately 8 hours.

b Hull – Rotterdam. The journey takes approximately 12 hours.

c Hull – Zeebrugge. The journey takes approximately 14 hours.

d Newcastle – Ijmuiden. The journey takes approximately 15 hours.

1 Draw lines on the map (right) joining the pairs of ferry ports, to show all 4 of the ferry routes.

2 Which is the shortest route?

3 Which is the longest route?

Look at photographs of Amsterdam in tourist brochures and books. Find the places mentioned above.

What is a grid reference?

4 people can play **Oranges and Lemons**.
You will need a die, and 6 counters for each player.

Look at the grid on sheet 2. First you need to know
how to locate objects on the grid. Each grid reference
refers to the bottom left corner of a square – like an
ordnance survey map. The letter is given first,
followed by the number. For example grid reference
A1 is an orange; grid reference E8 is a lemon. Give the
grid references for all the oranges and all the lemons:

oranges	lemons
A1	E8
. . . .	. . . .
. . . .	. . . .
. . . .	. . . .
. . . .	. . . .

The person to throw the highest number on the die
goes first. Take turns clockwise to play the game. To
start you must throw a 1, for verse 1 – St Clement's.
Give its grid reference correctly, then place a counter
on your grid. When your next turn comes you must
throw a 2 – St Martin's – and give its grid reference,
and so on. If you do not throw the right number, you
miss your turn. The first person to cover all six places
is the winner.

Look on an old map of the City of London – known as
the 'square mile'. Can you find the places in the
nursery rhyme? Shoreditch and Stepney are outside
the city wall.

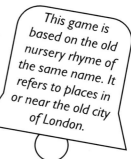

This game is based on the old nursery rhyme of the same name. It refers to places in or near the old city of London.

1 *Oranges and lemons*
    Say the bells of St Clement's

    Grid reference . . . .

2 *You owe me five farthings*
    Say the bells of St Martin's

    Grid reference . . . .

3 *When will you pay me?*
    Say the bells of Old Bailey.

    Grid reference . . . .

4 *When I grow rich*
    Say the bells of Shoreditch.

    Grid reference . . . .

5 *When will that be?*
    Say the bells of Stepney.

    Grid reference . . . .

6 *I'm sure I don't know*
    Says the great bell at Bow.

    Grid reference . . . .

7 *Here comes a candle to light*
    you to bed.
    Here comes a chopper to
    chop off your head.

Oranges and lemons

Look at Sheet 1 to find out how to play this grid game.

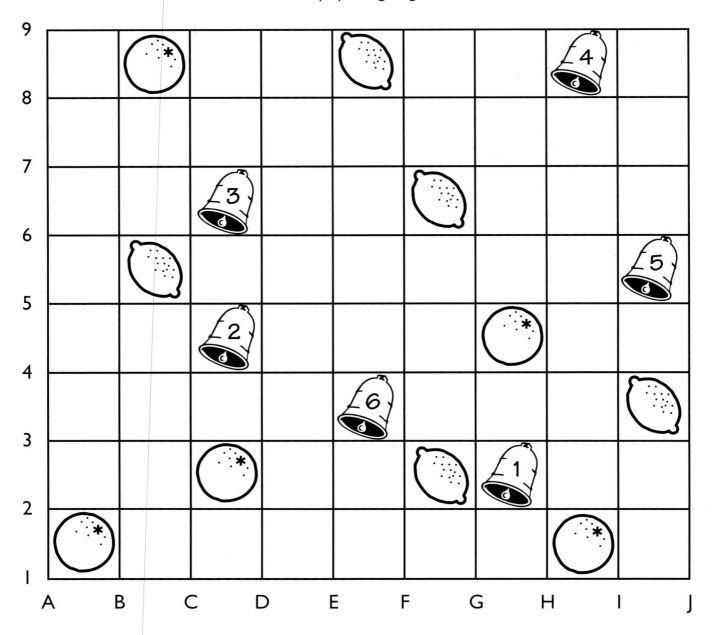

Note to teacher
This grid could be enlarged on to an A3 sheet.

How do I give a 4-figure grid reference?

The British Isles is mapped by the Ordnance Survey. It is divided into a grid of 100km squares. Each square is given an identifying letter. Then each 100km square is subdivided into 10km squares with numbered grid lines called *eastings* and *northings*. The 10km squares are subdivided into 1km squares and divisions east of eastings and north of northings are marked.

A 4-figure grid reference gives the easting first, followed by the northing. This reference marks the south-west corner of the square.

Grid references

a Colour the following grid references *red*:

   1 70, 02 **2** 70, 03 **3** 70, 04 **4** 70, 05
   5 70, 06 **6** 71, 04 **7** 71, 06 **8** 72, 06

   What letter can you see ? . . . .

b Colour the following grid references *yellow*.

   1 72, 02 **2** 72, 03 **3** 72, 04 **4** 72, 05
   5 71, 05 **6** 73, 05

   What letter can you see? . . . .

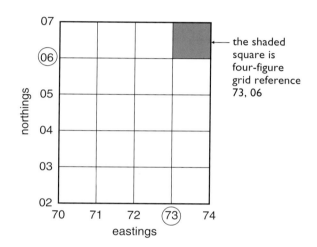

the shaded square is four-figure grid reference 73, 06

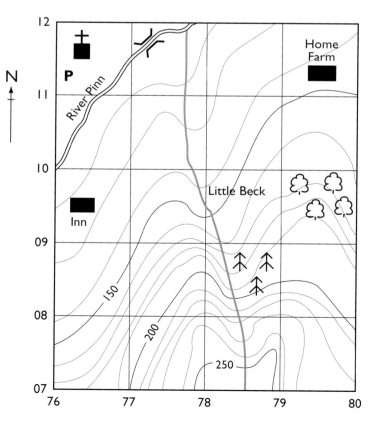

Colour the map.
Use *blue* for streams and rivers.

Write down the 4-figure grid reference for:

1 ⊤ a church . . . .

2 ■ an inn . . . .

3 ■ Home Farm . . . .

4 ⋏ a coniferous wood . . . .

5)(a bridge . . . .

How do I give a 6-figure grid reference?

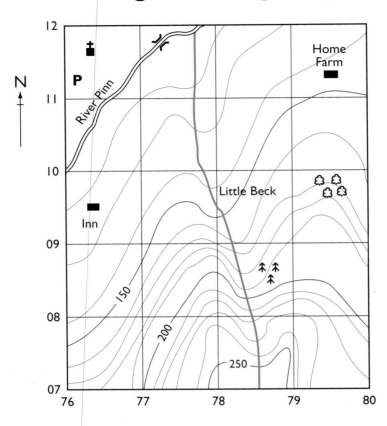

On this map, Little Beck joins the River Pinn at 4-figure grid reference 77, 11.

A more precise 6-figure grid reference can be given by imagining a grid lying over each square, creating 10 divisions along each axis.

On the map below, Little Beck joins the River Pinn at 6-figure grid reference 77<u>7</u>, 11<u>9</u>.

Estimate the six-figure grid reference for:

1 the church . . . .

2 the inn . . . .

3 Home Farm . . . .

4 the bridge . . . .

5 **P** the post office . . . .

Find your school on an OS map. Write down its 4-figure and 6-figure grid references.

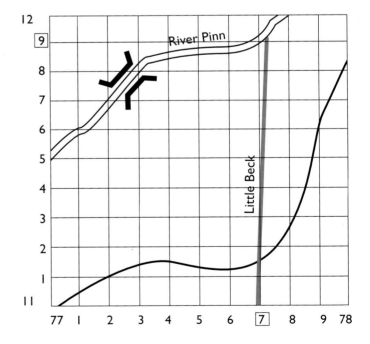

How should a map be labelled?

Look at a relief map of the British Isles in an atlas. Find one with a colour key. 'Read' the key to find out what each colour stands for.

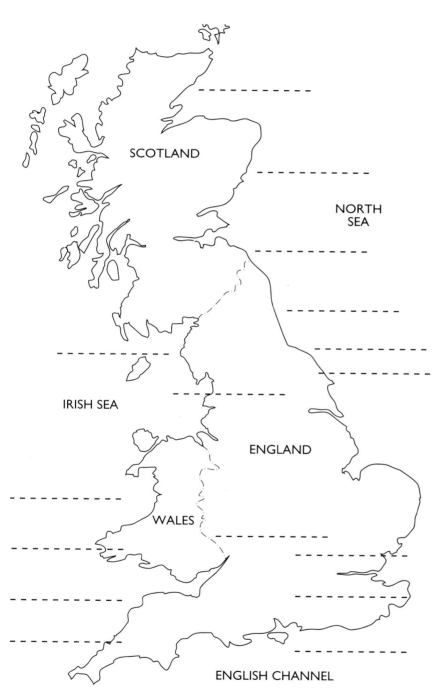

Now locate the following areas of high land on the atlas map:

Grampian Mountains, Cambrian Mountains, Pennines, Northwest Highlands, Southern Uplands, Cumbrian Mountains, Dartmoor, Exmoor, Cheviot Hills, Cleveland Hills, North Yorks Moors, North Downs, South Downs, Chiltern hills, Cotswold Hills, Brecon Beacons.

Draw and label the shape of these areas on your outline map. Colour them according to height above sea level.

Complete the colour key.

KEY
Land height above sea level in metres

☐ . . . . m   ☐ . . . . m

☐ . . . . m   ☐ . . . . m

☐ . . . . m   ☐ . . . . m

Remember to **print** neatly on your map.

 What is the difference between: *a mountain, a highland, an upland, a moor, a hill* and *downs*? Use a dictionary to help you.

 How do people use the highland areas of the British Isles? Think about work, leisure and energy.

What can we learn about settlement from place names?

Place names on maps can tell us about the past.

By looking closely at the place names you can discover something about the history of that area. Place names are clues left by the people who settled there a long time ago.

This map shows part of Cornwall, in southwest Britain.

 Look at the map and this chart. Then list all the place names you can find from the map that contain clues. What do the clues tell you?

Origin	Clue	Meaning
Danish or Viking	-by	farm or village
	-thorpe	farm or hamlet
Saxon	-ham	farm or hamlet
	-ton	farm or village
	leigh, lee or ley	forest or wood
Celtic	pen-	headland or hill
	tre-	hamlet
	-towan	sand dune
	-treath	shore
	-porth	harbour

Place names:

. . . .

. . . .

. . . .

. . . .

. . . .

. . . .

. . . .

. . . .

 Look at other place names, for example in Yorkshire and Hampshire. What do the names tell you about the settlement in those places?

How is information shown on maps?

Look at maps in an atlas. How is information shown? How is colour used? What kinds of symbols appear on maps?

Now use your atlas to fill in an outline map of the world.

First, highlight the coastline by shading in blue like this. Make horizontal lines using the side of your pencil, not the point.

Locate, then mark and name the following places on your outline map:

cities – London, Paris, New York, Buenos Aires, Cairo, Bombay (Mumbay), Sydney
indicate the location of each city with a square symbol like this:

rivers – Nile, Mississippi, Amazon
draw the shape of the river channel, then colour it blue, like this:

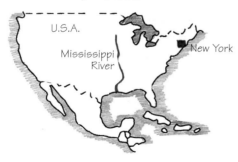

canals – Panama, Suez
indicate the location of each with a symbol, like this: = = = =

mountain ranges – Rocky Mountains, Andes, Himalayas
use hachuring like this to indicate the location of each; the darker the lines the steeper the slope.

deserts – Sahara, Kalahari, Gobi, Atacama
draw the shape of each desert area and colour it yellow

Remember to print neatly.

Devise a key for your map.

Look at the different kinds of lettering used on maps. When are upper case letters used? When are lower case letters used?

....

Do I understand geographical terms?

Look back through your completed worksheets or use a dictionary to help you find the right words. Fill in the missing letters to complete the words in the glossary.

1 a _ _ _ _ A book of maps.

2 b _ _ _ _ _ _ Compass direction.

3 c _ _ _ _ _ _ _ _ A large land mass, like Africa.

4 c _ _ _ _ _ _ A nation, like Kenya, with its own land and population.

5 d _ _ _ _ _ _ _ _ The course along which something travels, or lies; shown on a compass.

6 d _ _ _ _ _ _ The space between two places.

7 g _ _ _ _ A 3D revolving sphere on which the world's curved surface is represented.

8 k _ _ A list used alongside a map to explain colours and symbols; also called a *legend*.

9 l _ _ _ _ _ _ _ Distance north or south of the equator.

10 l _ _ _ _ _ _ _ The site or position of something.

11 l _ _ _ _ _ _ _ _ Distance east or west of Greenwich.

12 m _ _ A 2D diagram representing part or all of the surface of the world.

13 m _ _ p _ _ _ _ _ _ _ _ _ A representation of a 3D globe of the world on a flat piece of paper.

14 n _ _ _ _ _ _ _ g _ _ _ The imaginary network of 100km squares overlying UK and Ireland; an O.S map is made for the zone covered by each square.

15 o _ _ _ _ _ _ _ s _ _ _ _ _ The official map-making organisation for the UK and Ireland.

16 o _ _ _ _ _ _ _ _ _ _ _ Following a route using a compass; from the word 'orient' meaning east, once shown on all maps.

17 p _ _ _ _ _ _ A photograph, painting or drawing showing how something really looks.

18 p _ _ _ A 2D drawing of an object or place as seen from above.

19 s _ _ _ _ The relationship, or ratio, between the size of a real thing and the size of a drawing of it; used to draw maps and plans.

20 s _ _ _ _ _ Something that stands for something else; used on maps instead of words.

You can create your own glossary of geographical terms by adding new words to the list above. Place them in alphabetical order, like a dictionary.

What are latitude and longitude?

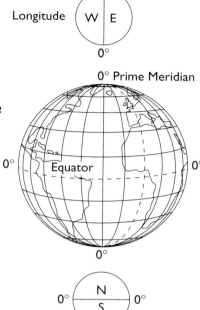

To fix position on a globe a network of imaginary lines is placed over the shape of the world. The axes of this grid are positioned exactly so that the world is divided into four equal segments. All positions in the world are calculated north, south, east or west from a fixed point (0,0) where the axes – Prime Meridian and Equator – intersect.

Lines of latitude are parallel with the equator.

Lines of longitude run at right angles to the equator, passing through both poles.

The equator is divided into 180° east and 180° west of 0 longitude - measured from the *centre* of the earth.

The North Pole is 90° north; the South Pole is 90° south.

The latitude of any point is measured by the angle formed between the point, the *centre* of the earth and the equator.

Complete the missing numbers and letters on the global grid below:

Lines are drawn at intervals of 20°

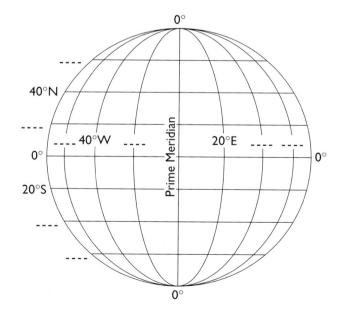

 Use an atlas to investigate and complete these sentences:

1 The line of latitude 23.5° north of the equator is called the

. . . . of . . . .

2 The line of latitude 23.5° south of the equator is called the

. . . . of . . . .

3 The 0° line of latitude is called the

. . . .

4 The 0° line of longitude is called the

. . . .

. . . .

5 The UK lies between the lines of

latitude . . . .° and . . . .°

 Look in the index of an atlas to see how latitude and longitude references are given.

How can the world be drawn on a flat map?

It is not possible to draw the real shape of the world on a flat piece of paper. Try flattening out the peel from an orange to see how difficult it is to turn a globe shape into a flat shape. Different map projections produce different maps. The lines and shapes are distorted. For example, lines of longitude on a flat map are equidistant, but in fact the lines of longitude come together at the poles. Lines of latitude all appear to be the same length, but in fact they are shorter near the poles.

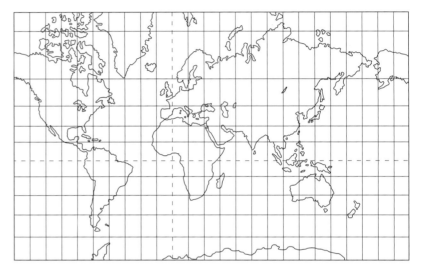

Investigate globes and map projections.

On a globe:

1 Do the lines of longitude meet at the poles? . . . .

2 Are the lines of latitude all the same length? . . . .

3 Which looks larger:

   a Africa or North America? . . . .

   b South America or Greenland? . . . .

On a projection map of the world:

4 Do the lines of longitude meet at the poles? . . . .

5 Do the lines of latitude all look the same length? . . . .

6 Which looks larger:

   a Africa or North America? . . . .

   b South America or Greenland? . . . .

What is a continent?

A continent is a large land mass. Look at an atlas to find the seven continents of the world.

I N _ _ _ _   A _ _ _ _ _ _ _   **2** S _ _ _ _   A _ _ _ _ _ _   **3** A _ _ _ _ _ _

4 A _ _ _   **5** E _ _ _ _ _   **6** O _ _ _ _ _ _   **7** A _ _ _ _ _ _ _ _ _

Look in an atlas and try to memorise the *shape* of each continent.

Now follow the colouring instructions below to reveal the shapes of two hidden continents. What are they?

A colour spaces 1– 25 in blue

   colour spaces 26 – 28 red

   colour spaces 29 – 32 yellow

   colour spaces 33 – 48 green

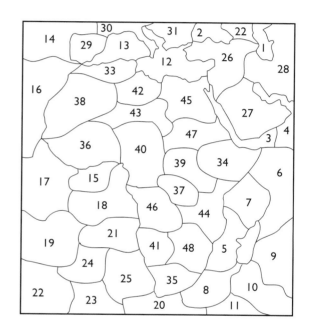

This is the shape of . . . .

Name one country in this continent.

. . . .

B colour spaces 1 – 22 blue

   colour spaces 23 – 24 red

   colour spaces 25 – 36 yellow

This is the shape of

. . . .

Name the largest country in this continent.

. . . .

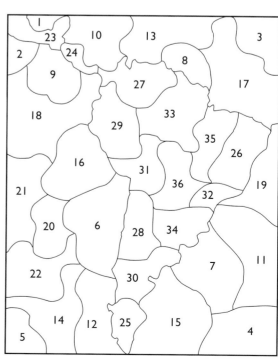

Look at the continents on a globe. Which is the largest? Now look at them on a map. Do the sizes look the same?

How do I use an atlas index?

Places in the world are listed alphabetically in an atlas index. After each entry is the country in which that place is found. Then the page number is given. This is followed by the number of degrees of latitude north or south of the equator, and the number of degrees of longitude east or west of the Prime Meridian.

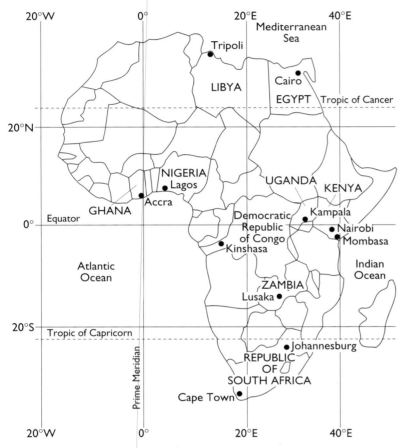

Accra, in Ghana, will be listed as being 06° N, 0°, because it lies 6° north of the equator, on the Prime Meridian. Each reference usually has a number *and* a letter.

Locations for every place in the world are made from the fixed point south of Accra, 0°, 0°: the point where the Prime Meridian and the Equator intersect.

 Find the positions of the African cities in the table below.

Check your answers in an atlas index

City	Country	Latitude	Longitude
Cape Town	Republic of South Africa		
Lusaka			
Kinshasa			
Nairobi			
Kampala			
Cairo			
Lagos			
Tripoli			
Mombasa			

How are places located by latitude and longitude?

The location of almost every place in the world is given in an atlas index, using numbers and letters that relate to specific lines of latitude and longitude.

Lines of latitude, or *parallels*, are numbered in degrees north and south of the equator. Lines of longitude, or *meridians*, are numbered in degrees east and west of the Prime Meridian.

For example, Paris, France, is located at 49°N 2°E

Shade around coastlines of this world map in blue.
Estimate the location of each of the following cities. Give the latitude first:

New York . . . .   Tokyo   . . . .   Wellington   . . . .

Chicago   . . . .   Lima   . . . .   Rio de Janeiro . . . .

London   . . . .   Accra   . . . .

Nairobi   . . . .   Moscow   . . . .

Now look up the exact locations in an atlas index. How close were your answers?

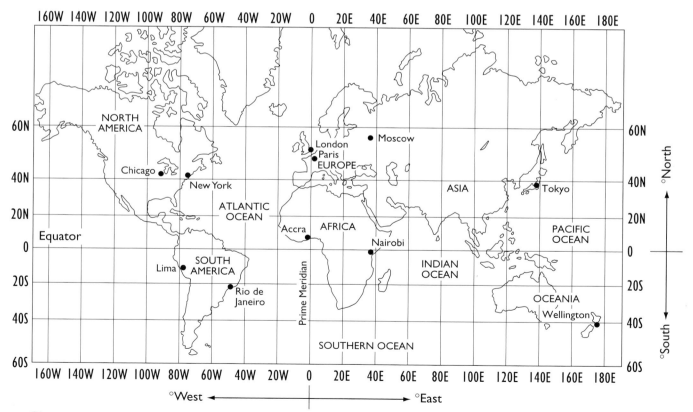

Mark and name the following cities on the map:

Algiers 37° N 3° E   Perth 32° S 116° E   Singapore 1 N° 104° E

Where is Kenya?

The huge continent of Africa is made up of 54 different countries. The country of Kenya is in East Africa.

Look at an atlas to locate Kenya. Kenya is in the _ _ _ _ of Africa.

Mark Nairobi, the capital, on Map A. Then:
colour Kenya green
colour Ethiopia yellow
colour Uganda red
colour Tanzania orange

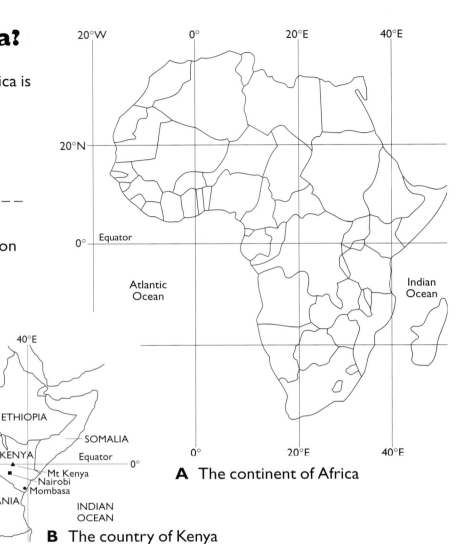

A The continent of Africa

B The country of Kenya

Complete these sentences about Kenya by looking at the maps above.

1 Kenya lies between the lines of latitude . . . . N and . . . . S.

2 Kenya lies between the lines of longitude . . . . E and . . . . E.

3 The capital city of Kenya is N _ _ _ _ _ _ .

4 The highest point in Kenya is M _ _ _ _   K _ _ _ _ .

5 In the SW corner of Kenya lies L _ _ _   V _ _ _ _ _ _ _ .

6 The . . . . border of Kenya is on the coast.

7 The port of M _ _ _ _ _ _ gives access to the I _ _ _ _ _   O _ _ _ _ .

8 Ethiopia is . . . . of Kenya.

9 Uganda is . . . . of Kenya.

10 Tanzania is . . . . of Kenya.

Look at the key, then colour the flag of Kenya.

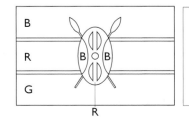

Key:
B = black
R = red
G = green

Is time the same all over the world?

Time is measured from Greenwich Mean Time (GMT), the standard time at Greenwich, London. Every 15° of longitude east of GMT means adding on one hour. Every 15° of longitude west of GMT means taking off one hour. Time must be adjusted 180° west and 180° east of the Prime Meridian on the International Date Line (IDL). Crossing this imaginary line – which does not pass through any land mass – from east to west means losing one day. Crossing from west to east means gaining one day. This means that there is a difference of one day between places either side of the line.

Time is the same across all of each time zone. Time changes when another 15° of longitude is crossed, although some are adjusted so that small countries are not divided into two time zones.

When the new millenium dawns on January 1, 2000, Chatham Islands, the first populated land mass west of the IDL, will experience it first.

 If it is 12 noon at Greenwich, what time is it in these cities? Use the 24 hour clock:

1 Los Angeles . . . .   5 Accra . . . .   9 Singapore . . . .

2 New York . . . .   6 Moscow . . . .   10 Tokyo . . . .

3 Rio de Janeiro . . . .   7 Nairobi . . . .

4 Sydney . . . .   8 Johannesburg . . . .

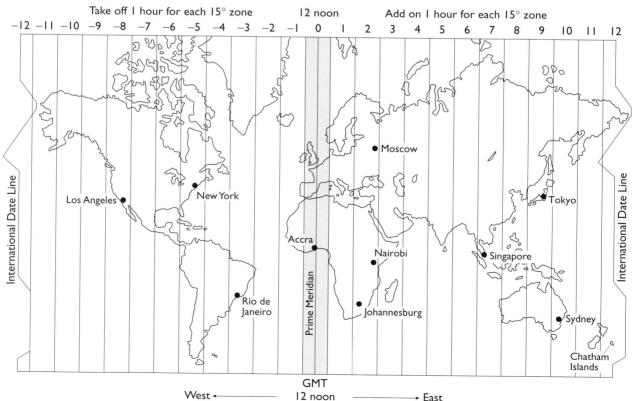

 Who needs to know the time in different parts of the world? Why?

What is the fastest route for a ship to circumnavigate the globe?

You are about to circumnavigate the globe in a sailing boat. Look at the entries in the log book. The weekly entries give the exact position of your boat. Chart every position on the map of the world, then draw in your route from start to finish.

Log book entries are at weekly intervals. During which weeks does the ship cross the equator?

1 . . . .   2 . . . .

During which week does the ship cross the International

Date Line? . . . .

LOG BOOK		
Day	**Position**	
1	51°N	1°W
7	18°N	25°W
14	11°S	28°W
21	37°S	15°W
28	40°S	45°E
35	43°S	109°E
42	47°S	175°E
49	47°S	108°W
56	46°S	45°W
63	14°S	20°W
70	17°N	33°W
77	44°N	28°W
80	51°N	1°W
BACK IN		
SOUTHAMPTON		

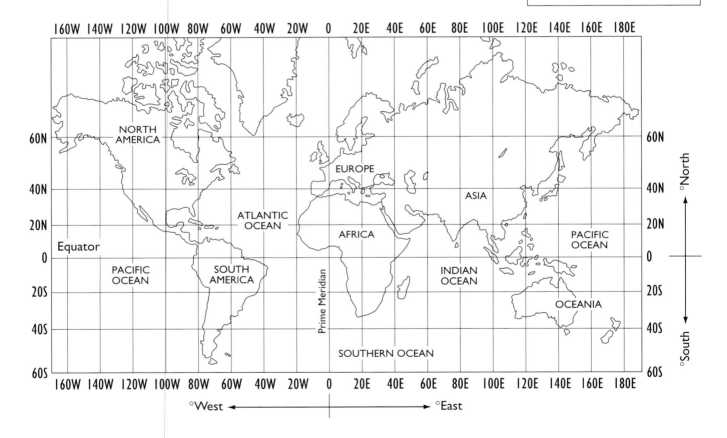

Find out about the prevailing winds by investigating a climate map of the world. In which directions do they blow?

Does climate affect land use?

Look at the key below. Each symbol stands for a crop grown somewhere in the world. Now look at the chart showing the names of the countries in which each of the 12 crops is grown. Use the symbols – or design your own – to show this information on an outline map of the world.

Then complete the chart by writing in the third column the name of the products made from each crop. In the last column indicate whether the crop grows in a tropical area or a temperate area, or both. Are the same crops grown in both tropical and temperate zones?

Crop	Country/continent	Product	Tropical/Temperate/both
1 wheat	N and S America, Russia, Europe, China, S Australia		
2 maize	N and S America, South Africa, Eastern Europe		
3 coffee	Kenya, Brazil		
4 sugar beet	Europe		
5 tea	India, Sri Lanka		
6 sisal	East Africa		
7 cotton	Egypt, Southern USA		
8 rice	SE Asia, Southern USA		
9 potatoes	Europe		
10 cocoa	West Africa		
11 grapes	France, Australia, Southern USA		
12 olives	Italy, Spain		

KEY

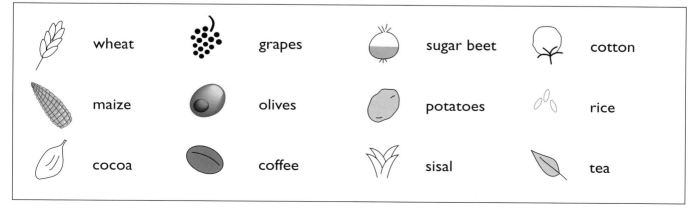

How far is it?

Investigate the outline map of Europe, on a separate sheet. Twenty cities have been marked. The scale of the map is 1:25000000 or 1cm stands for 250km. The *city of Prague* will be the *fixed point* from which distances to each of the other 19 cities will be measured.

Rule a line from Prague to each city.
Measure each line and estimate the *real* distance from Prague.

Chart your answers under the following headings:

City	Country	Distance
Amsterdam		
Athens		
Belfast		
Berlin		
Bonn		
Brussels		
Bucharest		
Copenhagen		
Helsinki		
Istanbul		
London		
Madrid		
Moscow		
Naples		
Paris		
Reykjavik		
Riga		
Stockholm		
Warsaw		

 What do you know about any of the cities on the map?
Choose a city you would like to visit. How would you get there?

Are rivers important to the growth of settlement?

Use an atlas index to locate the following rivers on a map of Europe. Then mark them on your outline map. Devise a key using numbers or letters instead of writing names on the map.

Thames, Seine, Loire, Garonne, Rhine, Rhone, Danube, Volga.

Complete the following chart:

River	Country or Countries through which river flows	Direction of flow
Thames		
Seine		
Loire		
Garonne		
Rhine		
Rhone		
Danube		
Volga		

1 The port of Rotterdam is situated at the mouth of the River . . . .

2 The cities of Paris and Rouen are situated on the River . . . .

Mark other major cities and ports that lie on the rivers you have shown on your map.

Discuss why a city or port might develop on or near a river.

What are the major causes of pollution in the world today?

Maps can convey important information about the environment. Wild animals all over the world are threatened with extinction. One of the major threats to marine and coastal fauna is oil pollution.

The Persian Gulf is surrounded by the major oil-producing countries of the world – Iran, Iraq, Kuwait, Saudi Arabia, Bahrain, and the United Arab Emirates. Oil tanker traffic in the Gulf causes major pollution. In 1991 deliberate sabotage of oil pipe lines, during the Gulf War, created massive pollution on land and in the sea. Animals threatened were flamingoes, dugongs, green turtles and hawksbill turtles, and dolphins, fishes and sea birds.

Use an atlas to create a pictorial map to illustrate this information clearly. Design a key.

Chart the following incidents of oil tanker spillages on an outline map of the world. Design your map to convey a strong visual green message.

Year of Oil spillage	Oil tanker	Area affected
1967	Torrey Canyon	S.W. U.K., Lands End
1978	Amoco Cadiz	N.W. France, Coast of Brittany
1983	Castillo de Bellver	S. Africa, Cape Town
1989	Exxon Valdez	N. America, Alaska
1990	Mega Borg	Central America, Gulf of Mexico
1992	Aegean Sea	Europe and Spanish Coast
1993	Braer	Scotland and Shetlands
1996	Sea Empress	Wales and Milford Haven

Investigate areas in your locality that are being damaged by pollution.

What can you do about pollution in your locality?

Answers

1 1a, 2b, 3c, 4a / Bird's eye view of a bicycle.

2

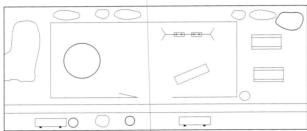

3 Even higher in the sky you would see a much larger area but less detail.
There are detached houses and terrace houses in Wigglethrop.
church supermarket school petrol station
Other kinds of homes in Britain include flats, bungalows, semi-detached houses, maisonettes, mobile homes (eg caravans). Homes in other parts of the world include houses on stilts, caves, flat-roofed dwellings, tents, etc.

4 Ratio of mouse or cat enlargement is 4:1, it is four times as big.

5 Box 1 is 4cm square; Box 2 is 3cm x 3cm; Box 3 is 5cm square. Box 3 is biggest.
Picture A is 16cm x 8cm; Picture B is 6cm x 3cm; Picture C is 18cm x 9cm.
Frame 1 is 6cm x 3cm; Frame 2 is 16cm x 8cm; Frame 3 is 18cm x 9cm.
Picture A fits Frame 2
Picture B fits Frame 1
Picture C fits Frame 3

6 *1a)* 90m *b)* 120m *c)* 180m
2a) 300m *b)* 450m *c)* 900m
3a) 1km *b)* 2.5 km *c)* 1.5km
4a) 4km *b)* 11km *c)* 21km

7 *1* 14cm/70m *2* 10cm/50m *3* 48cm/240m
4 10cm/50m *5* generator

8 The position of everything on the scale plan is the same as the sketch but it will look neater and bigger.

10 The sea is due east from the beach.
5 striped umbrellas; 3 flights of steps; 6 sandcastles; 3 seats

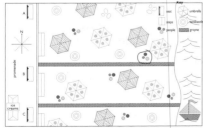

To buy an ice cream you walk SW.
From seat A you are looking SE to see the boat.

11 The following answers can only be estimated compass directions:
1 N *2* WNW *3* NE *4* SW
5 S; NW; NE; NNW; NW; NW

12 *1* 045° *2* 135° *3* 270° *4* 225° *5* 180°

school	2.5km	342°
memorial	3km	31°
station	1km	301°
church	2 km	36°
cinema	1.5km	201°
supermarket	1km	139°

13

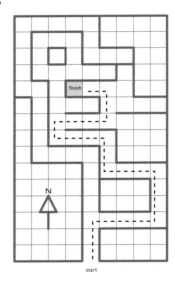

Into the maze

4 turn west, go forward 3 squares
5 turn north, go forward 2 squares
6 turn west, go forward 3 squares
7 turn north, go forward 1 square
8 turn east, go forward 3 squares
9 turn north, go forward 2 squares
10 turn west, go forward 2 squares

Out of the maze

2 turn south, go forward 2 squares
3 turn west, go forward 3 squares
4 turn south, go forward 1 square
5 turn east, go forward 3 squares
6 turn south, go forward 2 squares
7 turn east, go forward 3 squares
8 turn south, go forward 3 squares
9 turn west, go forward 4 squares
10 turn south, go forward 2 squares

14 *1* 800m *2* 650m

3 The shortest route from the police station to the school is to turn right in Green Lane, to reach the High Street, then right into Park Road. Then turn left into West End Lane and cross over the road. 600m.

4 Railway Station

5 Petrol Station

6a) Turn left and walk NW to the Main Road. Turn left and walk SW for 50m. Turn left into Station Road . Walk SE for 200m. Distance: 275m

6b) Turn right in Church Road and walk SE for 100m. Turn right into East View. Walk SW for 75m until you reach the junction with Station Road. Cross the road to the station. Distance 225m. Route b) is shorter.

7 Cross over the High Street and into Green Lane. Walk SE for 100m and turn right into Church Avenue. Walk 200m SW then turn left into Church Road. Walk 25m SE to the church entrance. Distance 350m.

15

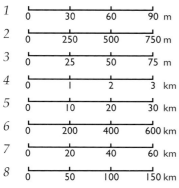

A street map is large scale. A map of the world is small scale.

16a (2 sheets)

    cliff

    bridge

    broad-leaved trees

    coniferous trees

    gate

16b The hill on which James lives is over 200m high. Ben Nevis is 1344m high.

17 *3* Anne Frank's house is NW of Dam Square.

4 The Van Gogh Museum is south of Anne Frank's house.

5 Rembrandthuis is SSE of the Central Station.

2 The shortest ferry route is Harwich to the Hook of Holland.

3 The longest ferry route is Newcastle to Ijmuiden.

18 (2 sheets)

Oranges A1: B8: C2: G4: H1

Lemons E8: B5: F2: F6: I3

Verse 1, St Clements, G2

Verse 2, St Martins, C4

Verse 3, Old Bailey, C6

Verse 4, Shoreditch, H8

Verse 5, Stepney, I5

Verse 6, Bow, E3

19 *a* F   *b* T

1 76,11   *2* 76,09   *3* 79,11   *4* 78,08   *5* 77,11

20 *1* church   764117   *4* bridge   772118

2 inn   764095   *5* P   761112

3 Home Farm 795114

21

Examples of definitions:

Mountain   a large natural elevation of the earth's surface rising abruptly from the surrounding level: a large steep hill.

Highland   an area of mountainous land

Upland   high or hilly country

Moor   open, uncultivated upland

Hill   a naturally raised area of land

Downs   an area of open, rolling land

24 *1* atlas   *2* bearing   *3* continent   *4* country

5 direction   *6* distance   *7* globe   *8* key

9 latitude   *10* location   *11* longitude   *12* map

13 map projection   *14* national grid

15 ordnance survey   *16* orienteering

17 picture   *18* plan   *19* scale   *20* symbol

25 *1* Tropic of Cancer

2 Tropic of Capricorn

3 Equator

4 Prime Meridian

5 50 north and 60 north

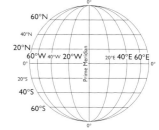

26 *1* yes *2* no *3a* Africa *3b* South America
4 no *5* yes *6a* North America *6b* Greenland

27 *1* North America *2* South America *3* Africa
4 Asia *5* Europe *6* Oceania
7 Antarctica
A Africa Any African country e.g Kenya
B South America Brazil
Asia is the largest continent. No, the sizes do not look the same.

28 Chart showing answers filled in:

Cape Town	Republic of South Africa	34°S	18°E
Lusaka	Zambia	15°S	28°E
Kinshasa	Zaire	4°S	15°E
Nairobi	Kenya	1°S	36°E
Kampala	Uganda	0°	32°E
Cairo	Egypt	30°N	31°E
Lagos	Nigeria	6°N	3°E
Tripoli	Libya	33°N	13°E
Mombasa	Kenya	4°S	39°E

29 New York 40°N 74°W Tokyo 35°N 139°E
Wellington 41°S 176°E Chicago 42°N 88°W
Lima 12°S 77°W Rio de Janeiro 22°S 43°W
London 51°N 0 Accra 5°N 0°W
Nairobi 1°S 36°E Moscow 56°N 37°E

30 Kenya is in the *east* of Africa (could be *continent*).
1 20° N and 20° S *2* 20° E and 40° E *3* Nairobi
4 Mount Kenya *5* Lake Victoria
6 Eastern *7* Mombasa/Indian Ocean *8* North
9 West *10* South

31 *1* 04.00 *2* 07.00 *3* 09.00 *4* 22.00 *5* 12.00
6 14.00 *7* 14.00 *8* 14.00 *9* 19.00 *10* 21.00

32 *1* 2nd week, between day 7 and day 14
2 10th week, between day 63 and day 70
It crosses the IDL during week 7, between days 42 and 49.
The prevailing winds are the Trade Winds in the tropics, blowing from the NE and SE, and the Westerlies.

33

wheat	bread	temperate
maize	polenta, mealie cornflakes	both
coffee	beverage	tropical
sugar beet	sugar	temperate
tea	beverage	tropical
sisal	string	tropical
cotton	cloth, t-shirts	temperate
rice	rice krispies,	both
potatoes	crisps, chips	temperate
cocoa	chocolate	tropical
grapes	wine,	temperate
olives	olive oil	temperate

34

City	Country	Distance (approximately)
Amsterdam	The Netherlands	700 km
Athens	Greece	1580 km
Belfast	N.Ireland	1480 km
Berlin	Germany	300 km
Bonn	Germany	500 km
Brussels	Belgium	720 km
Bucharest	Romania	000 km
Copenhagen	Denmark	660 km
Helsinki	Finland	1340 km
Istanbul	Turkey	1500 km
London	England	1040 km
Madrid	Spain	1780 km
Moscow	Russia	1700 km
Naples	Italy	1100 km
Paris	France	880 km
Reykjavik	Iceland	2600 km
Riga	Latvia	1100 km
Stockholm	Sweden	1100 km
Warsaw	Poland	560 km

35

Thames	England	E
Seine	France	NW
Loire	France	W
Garonne	France	NW
Rhine	Switzerland	NW
	Germany	
	Netherlands	
Rhone	France	S
Danube	Germany	E
	Austria	
	Eastern Europe	
Volga	Russia	S